big
NATE
GREAT MINDS THINK ALIKE

More

adventures from

LINCOLN PEIRCE

---

big NATE

GREAT MINDS THINK ALIKE

by LINCOLN PEIRCE

SCHOLASTIC INC.

ISBN 978-0-545-78455-9

12 11 10 9 8 7 6 5 4 3 2 1   14 15 16 17 18 19/0

Printed in the U.S.A.   40

First Scholastic printing, September 2014

IT'S SICKENING, THAT'S WHAT IT IS.

WHAT'S SICKENING?

JENNY'S GOT A CRUSH ON **ARTUR**, MY **ARCH-ENEMY**! IT'S SICKEN-ING! ABSOLUTELY **SICKENING!**

IT SICKENS ME, IT REALLY DOES. AND IF IT TURNS OUT THAT **HE** LIKES **HER TOO**, THAT'S GOING TO MAKE ME... MAKE ME...

...SICK?

YES! **YES!** EX**ACTLY!**

Peirce

GORDIE! DID THE NEW ISSUE OF "FEMME FATALITY" COME IN YET?

DELIVERED JUST A HALF-MINUTE AGO!

LET'S TAKE A LOOK AT THE COVER AND SEE IF THIS ONE'S WORTH YOUR HARD-EARNED $2.95!

"WILL THE FABRIC-EATING MICROBOTS OF DOCTOR POX DEVOUR FEMME FATALITY'S MIDRIFF-BARING TANK TOP AND MINI-SHORTS?"

I THINK I SPEAK FOR EVERY RED-BLOODED AMERICAN BOY WHEN I SAY: RING IT UP!

POW!

KA-CHING!

NATE, HAVE YOU CHECKED OUT THE NEW "MADAM BOMB"?

SORRY, GORDIE. NO INTEREST.

I HAVE ROOM IN MY HEART FOR ONLY **ONE** SUPER HEROINE: **FEMME FATALITY!** SHE **BURIES** ALL THE OTHER CHARACTERS!

SHE HAS A CERTAIN **QUALITY** ABOUT HER! A CERTAIN... A CERTAIN... UH... WHAT'S THE WORD?

"CLEAVAGENESS"?

PAGE SEVENTEEN, PANEL FOUR. ROWRRR!

I'M SORRY TO HAVE TO TAKE AWAY YOUR COMIC BOOK, NATE... BUT "FEMME FATALITY" IS JUST TOO... **PROVOCATIVE** FOR A BOY YOUR AGE!

BUT I'M NOT SAYING YOU CAN'T READ COMICS! **I** USED TO LOVE COMIC BOOKS AS A KID, **TOO**!

SO I DUG OUT A BOX OF **MY** OLD COMICS! YOU CAN READ **THESE** TO YOUR HEART'S CONTENT! THEY'RE **CLASSICS**!

"LITTLE LOTTA"

LOVE HER FRECKLES!

...SO I REALLY HAD NO CHOICE! I TOLD NATE HE WASN'T OLD ENOUGH TO READ THAT TYPE OF COMIC BOOK!

I WOULD HAVE DONE THE SAME THING.

I DON'T WANT HIM LOOKING AT SOMETHING SO... SUGGESTIVE!

THIS FROM A MAN WITH AN ANNA KOURNIKOVA SCREEN SAVER.

REALLY!

WELL, I'M A TENNIS FAN.

HEY, GORDIE.

HI, NATE. STILL BUMMIN' OUT ABOUT "FEMME FATALITY"?

OF **COURSE** I AM! WOULDN'T **YOU** BE, IF **YOUR** DAD HAD FORBIDDEN **YOU** TO READ THE WORLD'S GREATEST COMIC BOOK?

HE SAYS IT'S TOO **PROVOCATIVE!** HOW WOULD **HE** KNOW? HE'S NEVER EVEN **READ** IT!

SO YOU'RE GOING OUT WITH GORDIE?

YUP! WE'RE MEETING AL AND BECCA AT THE MOVIES!

WELL, THAT'S VERY NICE! I'VE ALWAYS LIKED THAT GORDIE! HE'S A NICE YOUNG MAN!

HE HAS A GOOD HEAD ON HIS SHOULDERS!

DING DONG

AND YET...

HI, ELLEN! IS NATE HERE?

SO YOU'RE GIVING VALENTINES TO ALL THE GIRLS IN SCHOOL WHO DON'T HAVE BOYFRIENDS?

YUP

MAY I ASK WHY?

WHY NOT? IT'S A GREAT WAY TO HOOK UP WITH SOMEBODY!

CAN YOU THINK OF A BETTER WAY TO LET THE LADIES KNOW I'M AVAILABLE? IT'S A PERFECT STRATEGY!

THAT'S NOT A STRATEGY, THAT'S A CARPET BOMBING.

HEY, YOU. HERE.

Peirce

WHAT ARE YOU READING?

THE COMPLETE BOOK OF WORLD RECORDS!

EVERY SINGLE PERSON IN THIS BOOK IS **FA-MOUS!** SO IF I CAN BREAK ONE OF THESE RECORDS, **I'LL** BE FAMOUS!

THERE'S GOT TO BE **SOME** RECORD IN HERE I CAN BREAK!

FLIP
FLIP
FLIP
FLIP
FLIP
FLIP

I WAS THINKING THIS WAS GOING TO BE A SLOW WEEK, BUT THINGS ARE LOOKING UP!

AH **HA!** "BALANCING BRICKS ON HEAD WHILE WALKING ON BROKEN GLASS"!

LONGEST BEARD... LARGEST BALL OF STRING...

WHY ARE YOU SO FIRED UP TO SET A WORLD RECORD?

I JUST WANT TO BE **FAMOUS**, THAT'S ALL! NOTHING WRONG WITH THAT, IS THERE?

I WANT MY NAME TO BE UP THERE IN THE BRIGHT LIGHTS! I WANT PEOPLE TO REMEMBER ME **FOREVER!**

HENCE HIS SELF-PORTRAIT IN THE SECOND-FLOOR BATHROOM.

...WHICH THE **JANITOR**, BY THE WAY, KEEPS **PAINTING OVER!!**

I GOTTA SAY, NATE, I'M FASCINATED BY WHY YOU'RE SO OBSESSED WITH SETTING A WORLD RECORD.

WHY THIS QUEST FOR FAME? WHY DO YOU HAVE TO BE THE **BEST** AT SOMETHING? ISN'T IT ENOUGH JUST TO BE **YOU**?

ARE YOU SEEKING APPROVAL? IS THERE A TRAUMA IN YOUR PAST YOU'RE TRYING TO COMPENSATE FOR? **OPEN UP**, MAN! **TALK** ABOUT IT!

RELEASE THE WOUNDED CHILD WITHIN!

⁛ SNORT! ⁛

THERE'S GONNA BE A WOUNDED CHILD, BUT IT'S NOT GONNA BE ME.

THE PROBLEM WITH TRYING TO BREAK A WORLD RECORD IS THAT YOU NEED SO MANY **PROPS** FOR ALL OF THEM!

I HAVE TO FIND A RECORD WHERE I WON'T NEED A TIGHTROPE OR A BED OF NAILS OR A ZILLION MARBLES!

FLIP
FLIP
FLIP
FLIP
FLIP
FLIP

WAIT! **HERE'S** ONE! "BURIED ALIVE"!!

ALL WE NEED IS A SHOVEL!

I'LL ALERT THE SCHOOL NURSE.

DAD, WILL YOU HELP ME SET A WORLD RECORD?

WHY NOT?

OK, I'M TRYING TO SET THE RECORD FOR MOST CONSECUTIVE HOURS WATCHING TV. THE COUCH IS MY HOME BASE.

SO, AT REGULAR INTERVALS, I'LL NEED YOU TO BRING ME SNACKS AND SODA, FLUFF MY PILLOWS, STUFF LIKE THAT.

KLIK!

OH, AND PRACTICALLY SPEAKING, I'LL NEED A FUNNEL AND AN EMPTY BOTTLE.

DAD?

Peirce

GREETINGS, GENTS! MY CARD!

YOUR CARD?

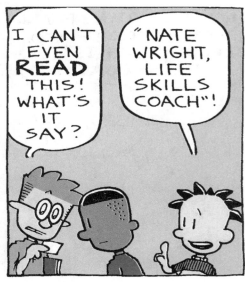

I CAN'T EVEN **READ** THIS! WHAT'S IT SAY?

"NATE WRIGHT, LIFE SKILLS COACH"!

DOES IRONY COUNT AS A LIFE SKILL?

CAN'T TALK NOW! I'M ON MY WAY TO DETENTION!

HOW DID **YOU**, OF ALL PEOPLE, DECIDE TO BECOME A **LIFE SKILLS COACH**?

I SAW A NEED, THAT'S ALL!

THIS SCHOOL IS FULL OF KIDS WHO NEED MY HELP! KIDS WHO HAVE NO SOCIAL SKILLS WHATSOEVER!

YOU'D BE **SHOCKED** TO LEARN HOW MANY KIDS THERE ARE AROUND HERE WHO ARE UTTERLY **CLUELESS!**

LESS SHOCKED THAN YOU'D THINK.

HEEEEY, BABY, GOT ANY FRIES TO GO WITH THAT SHAKE?

GREETINGS, FRIENDS! NATE WRIGHT, LIFE SKILLS COACH, AT YOUR SERVICE!

FOR A VERY REASONABLE FEE, I CAN HELP YOU ACQUIRE THE TOOLS YOU NEED TO WIN AT THE GAME OF LIFE!

NO PROBLEM CAN'T BE SOLVED! NO OBSTACLE CAN'T BE SURMOUNTED! IT'S ALL ABOUT BEING A CAN-DO PERSON AND HAVING A POSITIVE ATTITUDE!

AREN'T YOU THE KID WHO BURNED OFF HIS EYEBROWS IN SCIENCE LAB?

SEE, RIGHT THERE. THAT'S WAY TOO NEGATIVE.

GUYS, MEET MY FIRST LIFE SKILLS CLIENT! CHAD HERE WANTS HELP WITH HIS SHYNESS AROUND GIRLS!

TELL YOU WHAT, CHAD: AFTER SCHOOL WE'LL DROP BY CHEERLEADING PRACTICE AND YOU CAN TRY CHATTING WITH SOME OF THE LOVELY LADIES!

I CAN'T.

YES YOU **CAN**, CHAD! YOU'VE GOT TO THINK **POSITIVELY**! IF YOU **BELIEVE** IT, YOU CAN **ACHIEVE** IT!

NO, I CAN'T BECAUSE I HAVE "DUNGEONS & DRAGONS" CLUB.

A.H.

NOT MANY GALS AT **THOSE** MEETINGS!

Peirce

WHAT'S SHAKIN', BACON?

I'M TRYING TO TEACH MYSELF A MAGIC TRICK.

QUIET PLEASE

SHOW ME!

WELL, YOU'VE GOT THIS RUBBER BAND...

YOU LOOP IT AROUND YOUR INDEX FINGER, AND THE TRICK IS TO MAKE IT LOOK LIKE IT MAGICALLY JUMPS TO YOUR PINKY.

YOU'VE GOT TO SORT OF SECRETLY SLIDE IT OVER THE END OF YOUR PINKY, SEE...

...BUT I'M NOT SMOOTH AT IT YET. I CAN'T DO IT THE WAY YOU...

OOP!

ZING!

OGRAPHY

✦WHAP!✦

OW!

FOR MY NEXT TRICK, I'LL MAKE THE REST OF MY FREE PERIOD DISAPPEAR.

DETENTIO

46

LOOKS GOOD, GINA! YOU'RE REALLY WORKING HARD!

THANKS, MR. ROSA!

DID YOU HEAR **THAT**, NATE? MR. ROSA LIKES MY PAINT-ING!

OH, PLEASE.

THAT WAS A CLASSIC **PITY** COMMENT, GINA! WHEN HE TELLS YOU YOU'RE "WORKING HARD," HE'S SPEAKING IN **CODE**!

WHAT HE WAS **REALLY** SAY-ING WAS "YOU POOR, TALENTLESS..."

NICE, NATE! KEEP WORKING HARD!

Peirce

ARRRGH!

WHAT'S THE MATTER?

I JUST TOTALLY RUINED MY PAINTING.

NATE! WOW! I **LOVE** IT!

THAT PATCH OF BLUE IS **INSPIRED**! IT MAKES THE WHOLE PAINTING WORK! **GREAT** DE-CISION, NATE! VERY BOLD!

EITHER I'M AN ARTISTIC GENIUS, OR MR. ROSA IS A TOTAL HACK.

TELL YOU WHAT, NATE: **YOU** CONCENTRATE ON GETTING YOUR**SELF** CLEANED UP...

I'LL TIDY UP YOUR WORK AREA.

OK, MR. ROSA. THANKS.

THIS ISN'T A STUDIO, IT'S A SUPERFUND SITE.

...BUT DON'T MOVE ANY-THING.

I CAN'T BELIEVE I GOT DETENTION FOR **TARDINESS**! THAT'S JUST NOT A QUALITY DETENTION!

"QUALITY DETENTION"?

IS THERE SUCH A THING AS A QUALITY DETENTION?

OF **COURSE** THERE'S SUCH A THING AS A QUALITY DETENTION!

WHEN I SECRETLY CHANGED MRS. GODFREY'S CELL PHONE RING TONE TO "WEIRD AL" YANKOVIC'S "I'M FAT"... **THAT** WAS A QUALITY DETENTION.

HOW NICE TO KNOW YOU'VE GOT STANDARDS.

ACTUALLY, IT WAS A MONTH OF DETENTIONS. BUT IT WAS QUALITY.

HOW COME YOU'RE SO UPSET ABOUT GETTING DETENTION FOR TARDINESS?

BECAUSE TARDINESS IS **LAME!**

IT'S A WASTE OF A DETENTION! WHEN YOU GET DETENTION, YOU WANT TO GET IT FOR SOMETHING **WORTHWHILE!**

WHEN DAVID ORTIZ MAKES AN OUT, DO YOU THINK HE PREFERS TO DO IT BY CRANKING ONE TO THE WARNING TRACK, OR BY HITTING A FEEBLE POP-UP TO THE CATCHER?

AS YOUR LITTLE LEAGUE TEAMMATE, I MUST SAY THAT COMPARING YOURSELF TO DAVID ORTIZ IS A BIT OF A STRETCH.

I'M THE BIG PAPI OF DETENTION.

IT WAS SO TOUGH! I JUST COULDN'T GET THE NUMBERS TO WORK!

I SPENT ALMOST **TWO HOURS** ON IT!

AH!

☼CHUCKLE!☼... SOUNDS LIKE YOU GENTS HAD YOUR HANDS FULL WITH LAST NIGHT'S ALGEBRA HOMEWORK!

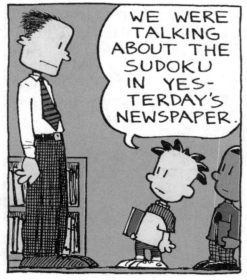

WE WERE TALKING ABOUT THE SUDOKU IN YESTERDAY'S NEWSPAPER.

OH.

WE HAD ALGEBRA HOMEWORK?

BEATS ME.

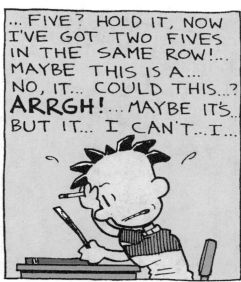

63

I HAVE NO IDEA WHAT THE LECTURE WAS ABOUT, BUT THE FELT-TIP PEN IN HIS SHIRT POCKET KEPT ME ENTERTAINED ALL CLASS LONG!

MAN, IT'S COLD!

THE THERMOMETER AT MY HOUSE SAID **TWENTY DEGREES** THIS MORNING!

HOOO! AND UP **HERE** IT'S EVEN **COLDER!**

YEAH! BECAUSE OF THE **WIND!**

THESE GUSTS HAVE GOT TO BE AT LEAST THIRTY MILES PER HOUR!

...WHICH MAKES THE WINDCHILL FACTOR **MINUS TEN!**

WAIT, WHAT?

THE **WINDCHILL FACTOR,** FRANCIS! YOU SUBTRACT THE WIND SPEED FROM THE TEMPERATURE!

ACTUALLY, CALCULATING THE WINDCHILL FACTOR ISN'T THAT SIMPLE. THERE'S A COMPLEX MATHEMATICAL FORMULA.

IF "T" MEANS TEMPERATURE AND "V" MEANS WIND VELOCITY, THE FORMULA GOES:
$3.74 + 0.6215T - 35.75(V^{0.16}) + 0.4275(V^{0.16})...$

BOOMP!

YAAAAAAA

I DON'T MIND THE WINDCHILL, BUT I CAN'T STAND A BLOWHARD.

I FEEL WARMER ALREADY!

OBSERVE, TEDDY, AS I DEMONSTRATE THE TRANSFORMATIVE POWER OF **FONTS!**

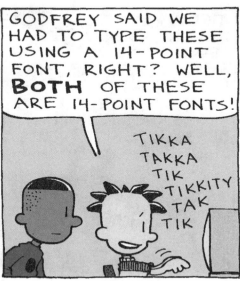

GODFREY SAID WE HAD TO TYPE THESE USING A 14-POINT FONT, RIGHT? WELL, **BOTH** OF THESE ARE 14-POINT FONTS!

TIKKA TAKKA TIK TIKKITY TAK TIK

The Boston Tea Party, which took place on December 16, 1773, was a very significant event in United States history.

The Boston Tea Party, which took place on December 16, 1773, was a very significant event in United States history.

IT... IT'S A **MIRACLE!**

AMEN, BROTHER!

TIKKA TIKKA TIK TAK

Peirce

TEDDY, YOU'RE NEVER GONNA MAKE IT TO THREE PAGES LIKE **THAT!**

WHAT DO YOU MEAN, "LIKE THAT"?

YOU CAN'T JUST WRITE "THE COLONISTS WERE MAD AT ENGLAND FOR TAXING THEIR TEA"! THAT'S TOO **SHORT!** YOU'VE GOT TO STRETCH IT **OUT!**

To say the colonists were up- set with England for taxing their tea is understating the matter. They were BEYOND upset. They were angry, irate, miffed, peeved, mad, furious, perturbed, enraged, ticked off, sore, chafed, cross, huffy, incensed, and generally splenetic.

TIK TAK TIK TIK

"SPLENETIC"?

Or, to put it another way,

70

I STILL DON'T THINK I'M GONNA BE ABLE TO STRETCH THIS TO THREE PAGES.

TEDDY, TEDDY, TEDDY!

YOU'RE WORRYING TOO MUCH ABOUT **CONTENT**! JUST STICK IN SOME RANDOM WORDS! MRS. GODFREY HAS TO READ SO MANY OF THESE RE-PORTS, SHE WON'T EVEN **NOTICE**!

And then, under cover of darkness, the colonists threw countless boxes of tea for two and two for tea, me for you and you for me, tea for two and me for you alone into the depths of Boston Harbor.

DUDE, AREN'T THOSE **SONG LYRICS**?

TRUST ME, SHE'LL BLIP RIGHT OVER IT.

HOW'S THE SOCIAL STUDIES REPORT GOING?

YOU'VE HEARD OF "DOCTOR PHIL"?

When King George III received news of the Boston Tea Party, he flew into a rage. "ARRRRR-RRRRRRRRRRRRRRRRRRRRR-RRRRRRRRRRRRRRRRRRRRRR-RRRRRRRRRRRRRRRRRRRRRR-RRRRRRRRRRRRRRRRRRRRRR-RRRRRRRRRRRRRRRRRRRRRR-RRRRRRRRRRRRRRRRRRRRRR-

RRRRRRRRRRRRRRRRRRRRR-RRRRRRRRRRRRRRRRRRRRRR-RRRRRRRRRRRRRRRRRRRRRR-RRRRRRRRRRRRRRRRRRRRRR-RRRRRRRRRRRRRRRRRRRRRR-RRRRRRRRRRRRRRRRRRRRRR-RRRRRRRRRRRRRRRRRRRRRR-RRRRRRRRRRRRRRRRRRRRRR-RRRRRRRRRRRRRRRRRRRRRR-

RRRRRRRRRRRRRRRRRRRRRR-RRRRRRRRRRRRRRRRRRRRRR-RRRRRRRRRRRRRRRRRRRRRR-RRRRGH!!" he cried.

CALL ME "DOCTOR FILLER"!

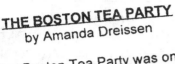

THE BOSTON TEA PARTY
by Amanda Dreissen

The Boston Tea Party was one of the most important events in our nation's history. It happened on December 16, 1773 in the city of

THE BOSTON TEA PARTY
Teddy Ortiz

One of the major events leading up to the Revolutionary War was called the Boston

THE BOSTON TEA PARTY
by Caitlin Embry

The Boston Tea Party is one of the first examples of the thirteen colonies fighting back against some of England's most

BEDLAM IN BEANTOWN!
by Nate Wright

It was quiet that night on the cobblestoned streets of Boston.
Too quiet.
The inky black waters of Boston Harbor lay like a

SIGH

Peirce

73

CAN I SEE THE COMICS PAGE?

HANG ON, TEDDY. I'M ALMOST DONE.

⁂TSK!⁂... BETHANY IS HAVING ANOTHER SPAT WITH GREG. WHAT DOES SHE **SEE** IN THAT....

YOU READ "BETHANY"?

MISTAKE.

DUDE, YOU READ "BETHANY"? THAT'S, LIKE, A COMIC STRIP FOR **GIRLS**!

WHA-?.. **NO**! I MEAN, I READ **ALL** THE COMICS!

SO YOU **DO** READ "BETHANY"!

WELL... OK, YES! BUT I DON'T PAY **ATTENTION** TO IT!

SO HOW COME YOU KNOW THE NAMES OF ALL THE CHARACTERS?

BECAUSE... I... IT... I... YOU... ✳SPUTTER!✳

FRANCIS! NATE READS "BETHANY"!

NO! SSH!

ISN'T THAT A CHICK STRIP?

NATE, I CAN'T BELIEVE YOU READ "BETHANY"!

✻SNICKER!✻... THAT'S THE WORST COMIC STRIP OF ALL TIME!

RIGHT! WHICH IS WHY I READ IT!

IT'S FUNNY TO SEE HOW **BAD** IT IS EVERY DAY! I MEAN, HAVEN'T YOU EVER LAUGHED AT SOMETHING JUST BECAUSE IT'S SO **PATHETIC**?

MMMPH!

HEH HEH

HA HA A HA HA HA HA A HA HA

WE HAVE NOW!

READING YOUR FAVORITE CHICK STRIP AGAIN?

I'M READING **ALL** THE COMICS, TEDDY! I CONSIDER MYSELF A COMIC-STRIP FAN!

IT JUST SO HAPPENS THAT **ONE** OF THOSE COMIC STRIPS IS ALL ABOUT... UH...

...ABOUT...

...THE LIFE AND LOVES OF A SENSITIVE TEEN-AGED GIRL?

IT'S GETTING HARDER TO DEFEND THIS.

LISTEN, TEDDY, STOP HARSHING ON ME FOR READING "BETHANY"!

BUT IT'S HILARIOUS THAT YOU'RE A FAN OF SUCH A LAME COMIC STRIP!

I'M NOT A **FAN**, I JUST READ IT BECAUSE IT'S **THERE**! IT'S LIKE... IT'S LIKE...

REMEMBER THAT WEEK YOU WERE HOME WITH STREP THROAT AND YOU ENDED UP GETTING ADDICTED TO "THE VIEW"?

SAY **WHAT**?

DUDE, YOU PROMISED.

I HAD A POINT TO MAKE.

WHEN YOU'RE TAKING A MULTIPLE CHOICE MATH TEST, IT'S ESSENTIAL TO HAVE A **PLAN OF ATTACK!**

STEP ONE: QUICKLY SCAN THE PAGE AND IMMEDIATELY ANSWER ALL THE EASY QUESTIONS.

STEP TWO: REPEAT STEP ONE WHILE TRYING TO IGNORE PERSPIR- ATION ON FOREHEAD AND NUMBNESS IN EXTREMITIES.

YOU CAN USUALLY TELL HOW KIDS ARE DOING ON A TEST BY WATCHING THEIR **BODY LANGUAGE!**

SOME ARE HAVING NO TROUBLES WHATSOEVER...

SOME ARE STRUGGLING A LITTLE BIT...

YOU
ACH

...AND SOME ARE FINISHED.

NATE, YOU SEEM TO BE STRUGGLING A BIT WITH MATH.

WELL... YEAH, I GUESS.

MR. STAPLES

I THINK YOU MIGHT BENEFIT FROM WORKING WITH A TUTOR.

A TUTOR? YOU MEAN LIKE A HIGH SCHOOL STUDENT?

NO, I ACTUALLY HAD SOMEONE ELSE IN MIND.

MR. STAPLES

HALLO! I AM REPORTED FOR TUTOR DUTIES!

ARTUR!!

Peirce

HOLD ON, MR. STAPLES! WHY DOES **ARTUR** HAVE TO BE MY MATH TUTOR?

YOU HAVE SOMEONE ELSE IN MIND?

HOW ABOUT OLIVIA BURBICK? **SHE'D** BE GOOD!

NATE, OLIVIA BURBICK IS WORSE AT MATH THAN **YOU** ARE!

WELL... YEAH, I KNOW, BUT...

...ROWR!

START HIM OUT ON CHAPTER FIVE.

Peirce

83

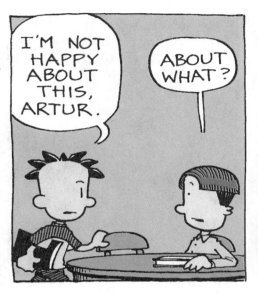

I CAN'T BELIEVE MR. STAPLES IS MAKING ME GET TUTORED BY **ARTUR**! WHAT A REVOLTING TURN OF EVENTS!

HEY! I JUST THOUGHT OF SOMETHING! WHAT IF I GET **WORSE** AT MATH INSTEAD OF **BETTER**?

THEN MR. STAPLES WILL **FIRE** ARTUR AND I'LL GET A **NEW** TUTOR!

EITHER THAT, OR YOU'LL FLUNK OUT OF SCHOOL ALTOGETHER.

...WHICH WOULD **ALSO** GET ARTUR OUT OF MY LIFE! I'M A **GENIUS**!

NATE.

HM?

WHAT DID I SAY TO THIS CLASS JUST BEFORE DISMISSAL YESTERDAY?

UH.... "GOODBYE"?

HEH HEH...

NO! I SAID "BEWARE THE IDES OF MARCH"!

WHAT'S THE IDES OF MARCH, NATE?

UMMM...

OOH!

THE IDES OF MARCH IS **TODAY!** MARCH 15TH!

VERY GOOD, GINA!

AND **WHY** WOULD I HAVE TOLD YOU TO **BEWARE** OF MARCH 15TH?

OOH!

BECAUSE YOU'RE GIVING US A SURPRISE TEST TODAY ON JULIUS CAESAR?

RIGHT **AGAIN!**

CLAP CLAP CLAP

PERSONALLY, I'M LOOKING FORWARD TO THE IDES OF JUNE.

ET TU, GINA?

GINA, I'VE COME UP WITH A NEW COMIC STRIP FOR THE NEWSPAPER! TAKE A LOOK!

"MRS. GOSLEY"?

THE HILARIOUS ADVENTURES OF A SADISTIC SIXTH-GRADE TEACHER!

IS THIS BASED ON ANYBODY WE KNOW?

DEFINE "BASED ON."

IS THIS MRS. GODFREY?

DEFINE "IS."

NATE, ARE YOU OUT OF YOUR **MIND**? WE CAN'T PRINT THIS COMIC STRIP IN THE NEWSPAPER! WE'LL GET **EXPELLED**!

WHY?

BECAUSE THIS "MRS. GOSLEY" CHARACTER IS SO CLEARLY BASED ON **MRS. GODFREY**!

WHAT? SHE IS **NOT**!

THERE ARE **MANY** DIFFERENCES! I MEAN, MRS. GODFREY IS A SIXTH GRADE SOCIAL STUDIES TEACHER!

MRS. **GOSLEY** TEACHES **MATH**!

RIGHT. STOP THE PRESSES.

LET ME GET THIS STRAIGHT, GINA: YOU WON'T PRINT MY COMIC STRIP?

YOUR COMIC STRIP ATTACKING MRS. GODFREY? NO, I **WON'T**!

THIS IS **CENSOR-SHIP**! "MRS. GOSLEY" DESERVES TO BE **SEEN**!

YOU THINK SO?

WELL, HERE COMES MRS. GODFREY. LET **HER** SEE IT.

RIP
RIP
RIP
RIP
RIP
RIP
RIP
RIP
RIP
RIP

ASH

GUYS, I'M NOT INTERESTED IN TRYING TO BEAT OUT GINA FOR THE "OUTSTANDING SCHOLAR" MEDAL.

FRANCIS! GINA NEEDS TO KNOW HOW IT FEELS TO FINISH **SECOND** FOR A CHANGE!

IF YOU WANT HER TO FINISH SECOND, NATE, WHY DON'T **YOU** TRY TO WIN THE "OUTSTANDING SCHOLAR" MEDAL?

MMPH!

HEH HEH... RIGHT.

HA HA HA HA HO HO HA

OKAY, OKAY!

THE BATTLE IS JOINED, GINA! THE BATTLE IS **JOINED!**

WHAT BATTLE?

THE BATTLE FOR THE "OUTSTANDING SCHOLAR" MEDAL! **FRANCIS** IS GONNA WIN THIS YEAR INSTEAD OF **YOU!**

SIT DOWN. LET'S DISCUSS IT.

SPLURCH!

DID I JUST SIT ON AN ICE CREAM SANDWICH?

THE BATTLE IS JOINED... BY A TOTAL **IDIOT!**

Peirce

IT'S ALL GOING TO COME DOWN TO THE SCIENCE FINAL, FRANCIS! IF YOU SCORE TWELVE POINTS HIGHER THAN **GINA**...

...THEN **YOU'LL** WIN THE "OUTSTANDING SCHOLAR" MEDAL!

FORGET IT, NATE! **NO**BODY CAN OUTSCORE GINA BY TWELVE POINTS!

WHAT? FRANCIS, YOU CAN'T THINK SO **NEGATIVELY!** DO YOU THINK LOUIS PASTEUR HAD THOUGHTS LIKE THAT BEFORE HE INVENTED MILK?

NO, I'M PRETTY SURE HE DIDN'T.

WELL, THEN. LET THAT BE A LESSON TO YOU.

SO LONG, DAD! I'M GOING OVER TO FRANCIS'S HOUSE FOR A STUDY SESSION!

GREAT!

I'M GLAD TO SEE YOU'RE GETTING READY FOR YOUR FINALS!

OH, WE'LL BE READY, ALL RIGHT!

...READY TO KNOCK THAT BRAINIAC **GINA** OFF HER PEDESTAL FOR ONCE IN HER SNOBBY, "I'M SMARTER THAN YOU ARE" **LIFE!**

STUDYING HAS CHANGED A BIT SINCE I WAS A BOY.

BWA HA HA HA HAA!

Peirce.

OKAY, GINA, SO YOU WON THE "OUTSTANDING SCHOLAR" MEDAL AGAIN! BUT FRANCIS **ALMOST** BEAT YOU!

OH, PLEASE!

YOU THINK I DIDN'T **KNOW** HE HAD TO BEAT ME BY TWELVE POINTS ON THE SCIENCE FINAL? I **LET** HIM BEAT ME BY **ELEVEN**! ON **PURPOSE**!

I THOUGHT IT WOULD BE FUN TO LET YOU CLOWNS THINK YOU ACTUALLY HAD A **CHANCE** TO TAKE MY MEDAL!

I DON'T KNOW WHETHER TO BE IMPRESSED OR FRIGHTENED.

OH, IS SHE EVIL.

...AND IF FRANCIS HAD OUTSCORED GINA ON THE SCIENCE FINAL BY TWELVE POINTS, HE WOULD HAVE BEATEN HER OUT FOR THE MEDAL!

UH-HUH...

...BUT HE OUTSCORED HER BY **ELEVEN**! IT WAS **SO** CLOSE! **THAT** CLOSE!

FASCIN-ATING.

...AND HOW DID **YOU** DO ON THE SCIENCE FINAL?

AS USUAL, HE TOOK THE CONVERSATION OFF ON SOME TOTALLY IRRELEVANT TANGENT.

Peirce

I LET A FROG LOOSE IN MR. GALVIN'S ROOM!

I PUT A WHOOPEE CUSHION ON MS. LA CHANCE'S CHAIR!

I SCANNED MRS. GODFREY'S HEAD ONTO THE BODY OF A SUMO WRESTLER, THEN SENT THE PICTURE TO EVERY COMPUTER IN THE SCHOOL DISTRICT DISGUISED AS AN URGENT MEMO FROM THE SUPERINTENDENT.

WE'RE IN THE PRESENCE OF "PRANK DAY" GREATNESS.

AMATEUR HOUR IS OVER, BOYS.

"SEE A PENNY, PICK IT UP, AND ALL THE DAY YOU'LL HAVE GOOD LUCK!"

HOLD IT!

WHAT?

IS IT HEADS OR TAILS?

WHAT DIFFERENCE DOES **THAT** MAKE?

A PENNY'S ONLY GOOD LUCK IF IT'S **HEADS!**

IF IT'S **TAILS,** IT'S **BAD** LUCK! DON'T TOUCH IT!

SO I'M JUST SUPPOSED TO LEAVE **FREE MONEY** LYING ON THE GROUND? I THINK **NOT!** I'M PICKING IT UP!

AND BY THE WAY, FRANCIS... IT WAS **TAILS!**

KRAK!

WONK!

OOH! HEADS UP!

Peirce

111

NATE! YOU ALMOST HIT ME WITH THAT FRISBEE!

SORRY, GINA, BUT THAT'S ONE OF THE HAZARDS OF BEING A SPECTATOR.

SPECTATOR? A SPEC-TATOR OF **WHAT?**

OUR FRISBEE GOLF TOURNAMENT!

YOUR **WHAT?** LOOK, I'M JUST TRYING TO **READ!**

THEN WHY ARE YOU SITTING IN THE MIDDLE OF THE TWELFTH FAIRWAY?

I HATE PEOPLE WHO DON'T LIKE SPORTS.

AH! **JENNY**, M'LADY!

EWWW! NATE, THAT'S **GROSS**!

WHAT'S GROSS?

YOUR **SHIRT**! YOU GOT **MOTION SICK** ON ONE OF THE RIDES!

NO, I DIDN'T! I HAVEN'T EVEN **GONE** ON ANY RIDES YET!

HE'S JUST A SLOB!

LOOK, IS IT **MY** FAULT THEY OVER-STUFFED MY CHILI DOG?

SCHOOL PICTURE GUY! YOU'RE THE SCHOOL PICTURE GUY!

OKAY, KID, OKAY. GUILTY AS CHARGED.

DUDE, HOW COME YOU'RE A **CLOWN**?

LOOK, I'M NOT PROUD OF IT...

...BUT A MAN'S GOT TO PUT **FOOD** ON THE TABLE, AMIGO! A MAN'S GOT TO PAY THE **RENT**!

RENT?

BUT DON'T YOU LIVE IN YOUR MOTHER'S BASE-MENT?

I MEANT RENT IN THE META-PHORICAL SENSE, KID. HAVE A GIRAFFE.

THIS IS GOING TO BE **EPIC**!

TEDDY, TOSS THE BALL JUST AS I'M HITTING THE TRAMPOLINE!

RIGHT!

I'LL THROW DOWN A TOMAHAWK DUNK FOR THE MOST SPECTACULAR ALLEY-OOP IN SPORTS HISTORY!

...AND FRANCIS, GET THE WHOLE THING ON VIDEO! WE'LL PUT THIS PUPPY ON YOUTUBE!

WE'RE ROLLING!

OKAY, THEN! **HERE WE GO!!**

ALLEY!...

CLANNG!

...OOP.

WE CAN STILL PUT THIS ON YOUTUBE, BUT INSTEAD OF "SPORTS," WE'LL POST IT UNDER "COMEDY."

Peirce

HI, IS THIS CHANNEL 12 CHIEF METEOROLOGIST WINK SUMMERS? WINK! NATE WRIGHT HERE!

LISTEN, WINK, DURING YOUR FORECAST LAST NIGHT, YOU SAID TODAY WAS GOING TO BE A "GREAT BEACH DAY"!

WELL, I'M CALLING FROM THE BEACH, WINK, AND I'M HERE TO TELL YOU THAT IT'S A **LOUSY** BEACH DAY!

WHAT? NO, NO, THE WEATHER'S FINE.

I'M TALKING ABOUT THE FACT THAT FRANCIS REFUSES TO SHARE ANY OF HIS SOUR CREAM 'N ONION "PRINGLES."

HELLO?

LISTEN, WINK, AS LONG AS I'VE GOT YOU ON THE PHONE, LET ME LAY THIS SUGGESTION ON YOU:

DURING YOUR WEATHER FORECASTS, HOW ABOUT THROWING IN A **JOKE** NOW AND THEN? YOU KNOW, DROP A LITTLE **HUMOR** IN THERE!

I MEAN, RIGHT NOW THE ONLY THING FUNNY ABOUT THE NEWS IS THAT LAME **TOUPEE** OF YOURS!

"THAT'S MY REAL HAIR!" **GOOD** ONE, WINK!

THEY PROBABLY DON'T TELL YOU ABOUT STUFF LIKE THIS IN METEOROLOGY SCHOOL.

GOOD GRAVY! ARE YOU EATING **AGAIN?** THAT'S YOUR THIRD SNACK THIS AFTERNOON!

EASE **UP**, NATE! IT'S NOT HEALTHY TO STUFF FOOD INTO YOUR MOUTH WHENEVER YOU'VE GOT NOTHING ELSE TO DO!

FATHERLY CONCERN, DAD? OR... **JEALOUSY?**

PAT PAT

JEALOUSY.

EATING **AGAIN**? DAD, **MY** EATING IS NOT THE ISSUE! WHEN YOU HARSH ON **MY** EATING, YOU'RE WORRIED ABOUT YOUR **OWN** WEIGHT!

WHY NOT JUST GO ON A **DIET**, DAD? SET YOURSELF A GOAL, THEN **GO** FOR IT!

WHAT'S THE MAGIC NUMBER, DAD? HOW MUCH WEIGHT DO YOU WANT TO LOSE?

AT THE MOMENT, ABOUT EIGHTY-SIX POUNDS.

REALLY? WOW, THAT'S HOW MUCH **I**..... HEY! **HEY!** WAS THAT A **SHOT?**

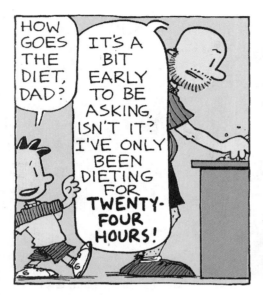

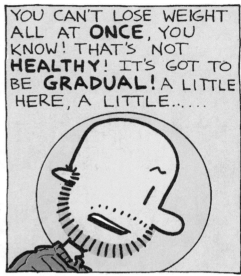

BLISTER, DAD?

A FEW OF 'EM. I JUST SPENT ABOUT FOUR HOURS CHOPPING WOOD.

HEY, **I'VE** GOT A BLISTER, **TOO!** A **BRUTAL** ONE ON MY THUMB, SEE?

WHAT A COINCIDENCE, EH, DAD? WE'VE BOTH GOT BLISTERS! SYMPATHETIC INJURIES, RIGHT?

EXCEPT I DIDN'T GET MINE PLAYING NINTENDO AT TEDDY'S HOUSE.

IT'S AN X-BOX, DAD. NINTENDO IS SO NINETIES.

Peirce

IT'S HOT. IT'S BOILING HOT. HEAT STRESSES ME OUT.

...BUT I CAN ALWAYS GET RID OF MY STRESS BY HITTING MYSELF GENTLY ON THE HEAD WITH AN EMPTY PLASTIC BOTTLE!

THUNK
THUNK
THUNK
THUNK
THUNK
THUNK

IT MELTED TO HIS HEAD!

I MAY SNAP.

I'M FREAKIN' OUT!... I'M FREAKIN' OUT!!

Peirce

IT'S NOT THE HEAT, IT'S THE INSANITY.

I'M FREAK-IN' OUT!

HERE'S THE REALITY, MR. EUSTIS: I CAN'T KEEP MOWING LAWNS IF MY **HEART'S** NOT IN IT!

THE GREAT ONES KNOW WHEN IT'S TIME TO SAY GOODBYE, AND **THIS** IS **MY** TIME!

I MEAN, IF **NOLAN RYAN** HAD KNOWN WHEN TO HANG UP HIS SPIKES, MAYBE HE'D BE IN THE **HALL OF FAME!**

NOLAN RYAN **IS** IN THE HALL OF FAME.

OKAY, WHATEVER. THE POINT IS, I'M SICK OF MOWING LAWNS.

I CAN TELL YOU'RE CONFUSED BY MY DECISION TO QUIT LAWN MOWING, MR. EUSTIS, BUT TRY TO LOOK AT IT FROM **MY** PERSPECTIVE!

I USED TO **LIKE** MOWING LAWNS, BUT GRADUALLY I'VE REACHED THE POINT WHERE I **HATE** IT!

LIFE'S NOT FUN WHEN YOU DON'T LIKE YOUR WORK.

...SAID THE ELEVEN-YEAR-OLD BOY TO THE MAN WHO'S SPENT THIRTY-ONE YEARS AS A SHORT-TERM DIS-ABILITY INSURANCE CLAIMS ADJUSTER.

YAK YAK YAK YAK YAK

ALL RIGHT, NATE, I GUESS I CAN ACCEPT THE FACT THAT YOU'RE QUITTING THE LAWN-MOWING BUSINESS...

...BUT I **CAN'T** ACCEPT THAT YOU'RE WALKING AWAY AND LEAVING MY LAWN ONLY **HALF-MOWED!**

OKAY, OKAY...

I SEE YOUR POINT, MR. EUSTIS. TELL YOU WHAT: I'LL GIVE YOU A 10% DISCOUNT!

❊ SIGH... ❊

HEY, IT'S MY PLEASURE. I'LL WRITE UP AN INVOICE!

152

YOU KNOW, JENNY, IT WOULDN'T KILL YOU TO BE **NICE** TO ME EVERY ONCE IN A WHILE!

WHY CAN'T YOU GIVE ME THE TIME OF DAY?

IT'S ONE-THIRTY. TIME FOR YOU TO GET OUT OF MY FACE.

SHE'S VERY PUNCTUAL.

Peirce

YEAH, HI. COULD I SPEAK TO CHIEF METEOROLOGIST WINK SUMMERS?

SURE, I'LL TAKE HIS VOICE MAIL.

HI, WINK. NATE WRIGHT HERE. YOUR ACCU-WEATHER FORECAST FOR TODAY, I DO BELIEVE, CALLED FOR A HIGH TEMPERATURE OF 87°.

INSTEAD, FOR THE THIRD DAY IN A ROW, IT IS A COOL AND BREEZY 101!!

YOU'RE KILLING US!!

I'D STOP HIM, BUT I'M TOO HOT.

HI, IS THIS CHIEF METEOROLOGIST WINK SUMMERS?... YEAH, THIS IS NATE WRIGHT. I LEFT YOU A VOICE MAIL YESTERDAY.

WHAT'S UP WITH THESE FORECASTS, MAN? YOU KEEP SAYING THIS HEAT WAVE IS GONNA **STOP** AND IT JUST KEEPS GOING ON AND **ON!**

YOU KEEP **RAISING** MY HOPES, THEN **DASHING** THEM TO **PIECES** WITH YOUR **METEOROLOGICAL INCOMPETENCE!**

WINK, YOU'RE NO AL ROKER.

OUCH.

Peirce

LISTEN, WINK, DON'T ACT LIKE THIS IS THE FIRST FORECAST YOU GOT WRONG. YOU SCREW UP **ALL THE TIME!**

DOES **DECEMBER 13TH, 2002,** RING ANY BELLS? YES, THAT'S RIGHT, WINK! THE " **STORM OF THE CENTURY** " WHICH AMOUNTED TO EXACTLY **ONE INCH OF SNOW!**

YOU HAD ME PRIMED FOR A **SNOW DAY,** WINK, AND **INSTEAD** I GOT SLAMMED WITH A **MATH TEST!!** AND YOU KNOW WHAT I **GOT** ON THAT MATH TEST??

TAKE A **GUESS,** WINK! YOU'RE **GOOD** AT THAT!!

HE HAS TROUBLE LETTING THINGS GO.

Peirce

HEY, LET ME ASK YOU, WINK: WHAT'S YOUR **REAL** NAME?

BECAUSE THERE'S NO WAY YOU WERE **BORN** WITH THE NAME "WINK SUMMERS," AM I RIGHT? WHAT'S WRONG, IS YOUR REAL NAME SO GOOFY THAT YOU...

OKAY, YOU'RE RIGHT. SAYING "CHIEF METEOROLOGIST DICK SCHIPP" ON LIVE TV **IS** PLAYING WITH FIRE.

LISTEN, WINK, SINCE I'VE GOT YOU ON THE PHONE, LET ME ASK YOU: WHY DO YOU CALL YOUR-SELF "WINK SUMMERS, **CHIEF** METEOROLOGIST"?

I MEAN, WHAT'S WITH THE "CHIEF", HUH? IS THAT SOME SORT OF **STATUS** THING DOWN THERE AT THE TV STATION?

BECAUSE LET ME TELL YOU, MY FRIEND, CALL-ING YOURSELF "**CHIEF**" DOESN'T MAKE YOU MORE IMPORTANT THAN THE NEWS GUY OR THE SPORTS GUY, OR **ESPECIALLY** THE LADY WHO REVIEWS MOVIES!

SPEAKING OF WHICH... COULD I SPEAK TO HER, PLEASE?

TIME TO HANG UP, SON.

Peirce

AH! **JENNY**, M'LADY!

"PALM READING"?

WHAT DO **YOU** KNOW ABOUT PALM READING?

A LOT! I GOT A BOOK ABOUT IT!

PALM $1

FORGET IT. THIS IS JUST ANOTHER ONE OF YOUR RIP-OFFS.

NO! WAIT!

I'LL READ YOUR PALM FOR **FREE**!

FREE?

PALM READING $1

EXACTLY! IF IT'S **FREE**, IT CAN'T BE A 'RIP-OFF, RIGHT?

I GUESS NOT...

OKAY, THEN! HERE WE GO!

PALM READING $1

MM-HM... MMM-HMM... MMMMMMM...

PALM READING $1

THIS COSTS TOO MUCH.

ROWR!

THIS IS BUMMIN' ME OUT.

WHAT IS?

ALL THESE **BACK-TO-SCHOOL** SIGNS! THEY'RE **EVERY**-WHERE!

I MEAN, CAN'T WE ENJOY OUR LAST FEW DAYS OF SUMMER WITHOUT SEEING THESE DISGUSTING REMINDERS OF **SCHOOL** ALL OVER THE PLACE?

HELLO, KIDS.

NYAA!

NATE! WHAT'S UP?

I NEED TO CLEANSE MY PALATE, GORDIE.

IC KOMIX

I JUST SAW MY TEACHER **MRS. GODFREY** OVER BY THE SHOE STORE! MY WHOLE DAY WAS IMMEDIATELY **RUINED!**

FORTUNATELY, "KLASSIC KOMIX" IS RIGHT HERE TO PROVIDE THE PERFECT ANTIDOTE: **GREAT LITERATURE!**

NATE, EVEN **I** DON'T CALL IT "GREAT LITERATURE," AND I **WORK** HERE.

AHHHHHH... "FEMME FATALITY"!...

On Labor Day,
We celebrate
The hands that built this land:

That dug the ditches,
Shoveled coal,
And tilled the soil and sand.

WORK AREA

The hands that fought,
The hands that healed,
The hands that held the tools...

But must we
Celebrate the hands
That built these stinkin' schools?

PUBLIC SCHOOL 38
BUILT 1912

WELCOME BACK,
STUDENTS

SEPTEMBER...
OCTOBER...
NOVEMBER...
DECEMBER...
JANUARY...

FIVE MONTHS! WITH MRS. GODFREY ON SABBATICAL UNTIL FEBRUARY, WE WON'T LAY EYES ON HER FOR **FIVE MONTHS!**

FIVE MONTHS WITHOUT MRS. GODFREY! FIVE WHOLE MONTHS! FIVE GLORIOUS MONTHS!

YOU'RE DROOLING.

AM I?

MR. ROSA! YOU HEARD THE GOOD NEWS?

HM? YES, I HEARD THE GOOD NEWS.

AH-**HA!** I DIDN'T EVEN SAY WHAT THE "GOOD NEWS" **WAS**, BUT YOU **KNEW** I WAS TALKING ABOUT MRS. GODFREY'S SABBATICAL!

...WHICH MEANS THAT **YOU'RE** HAPPY TO SEE HER GO, **TOO! YOU** PROBABLY HATE HER AS MUCH AS **WE** DO!

YOU'RE ONE OF US!

I THOUGHT HE WAS TALKING ABOUT THE CAFETERIA SERVING TATER TOTS.

OKAY, GANG, WE'LL BE WATCHING A FILMSTRIP THIS MORNING...

YES! YES!

THIS IS WHY YOU'RE SO MUCH BETTER THAN MRS. GODFREY! **SHE** ALWAYS GAVE US A **QUIZ** ON THURSDAY MORNINGS!

DID SHE NOW! HMM...

ACTUALLY, THAT MAKES A LOT OF SENSE, SINCE WEDNESDAYS ARE OUR CHAPTER REVIEW DAYS... YES, THAT MAKES **PERFECT** SENSE!

CLEAR YOUR DESKS, PEOPLE!

NICE MOVE, DORKUS.

HOW ARE THINGS GOING, PHIL?

GREAT! I REALLY ENJOY 6TH GRADERS!

IT'S A FUN AGE, YOU KNOW? THEY'RE 10! THEY'RE 11! THEY'RE STILL **KIDS!**

THEY'RE NOT SELF-CONSCIOUS! THEY'LL TRY ANYTHING! THEY'LL SAY ANYTHING!

MR. **GAFF**NEY! GAFFER! GAFFS! T'SUP, SLICE?

OF COURSE, THERE'S A LOT TO BE SAID FOR BROODING, SILENT TEENS...

HEY, WHAT'S WITH THE BEARD, BY THE WAY? ARE YOU AMISH?

NATE. HOW COME YOU'RE NOT SITTING DOWN?

BECAUSE, TEDDY, I'M GOING TO EAT AT THE TABLE IN THE CORNER!

SAY WHAT?

THAT'S WHERE THE SEVENTH GRADE GIRLS SIT!

EXACTLY! MAYBE THEY WANT SOME COMPANY!

SOMETIMES IN LIFE YOU'VE JUST GOT TO AIM HIGH!

WHEN THE GIRLS ARE ALL A FOOT TALLER THAN YOU, WHERE ELSE CAN YOU AIM?

HEY, HEY! NO SHORT JOKES!

NATE, ARE YOU ACTUALLY GOING TO TRY SITTING OVER THERE WITH THE SEVENTH GRADE GIRLS?

WHY NOT?

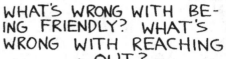

WHAT'S WRONG WITH BEING FRIENDLY? WHAT'S WRONG WITH REACHING OUT?

PICKETT'S CHARGE?

I WAS THINKING LITTLE BIGHORN.

WHAT'S SO FUNNY?

HEE HEE! NATE JUST TRIED TO SIT WITH THE SEVENTH GRADE GIRLS!

SO **WHAT**? WHAT'S THE BIG DEAL?

YOU GUYS ACT LIKE THEY'RE **SUPERMODELS!** THEY'RE JUST **PEOPLE!** THEY PUT THEIR PANTS ON ONE LEG AT A... UH...

LEG... UM... PANTS...

SUAVE. VERY SUAVE.

LEGS...

DAD, I MADE A LIST OF ALL THE CANDY I WANT US TO HAND OUT THIS HALLOWEEN!

LET'S HAVE A LOOK!

SNICKERS®, MILKY WAYS®, BUTTERFINGERS®, SKITTLES®, JUNIOR MINTS®... ALL THE **CLASSICS!**

HMM... WE'VE GOT A PROBLEM, NATE...

ALL THESE CANDIES CONTAIN **SUGAR.**

I'M BEGINNING TO GET THAT SPOOKY FEELING.

PLUS, THEY HAVE ALMOST **NO** DIETARY FIBER.

Peirce

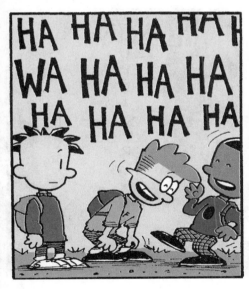

YOU KNOW, THE CARTOONING CLUB JUST ISN'T AS FUN THESE DAYS.

WHATTA YA MEAN?

WELL, I USED TO SPEND ALL THE MEETINGS DRAWING INSULTING CARTOONS ABOUT MRS. GODFREY... BUT WITH HER ON SABBATICAL, THAT JUST SEEMS... I DUNNO.... HOLLOW.

YOU MISS MRS. GODFREY!

HUH? NO, I DON'T, I...

NATE MISSES MRS. GODFREY!!

SHUT UP! SHUT UP!

WHAT'S THIS ABOUT NATE MISSING MRS. GODFREY?

HE DOES!

NO, I **DON'T**!

ALL I'M SAYING IS THAT WITH HER ON SABBATICAL, I CAN'T MAKE **FUN** OF HER ANYMORE!

I DON'T MISS **HER**, I MISS BEING ABLE TO **BUST** ON HER, BECAUSE I **HATE** HER SO MUCH!

BUT IT'S A FINE LINE BETWEEN **HATE** AND **LOVE**!

OOOOOOOH!

EVEN ON SABBATICAL, SHE'S RUINING MY LIFE.

YOU SEE, INSULTING MRS. GODFREY WHEN SHE'S NOT AROUND MEANS THERE'S NO **RISK** INVOLVED! THERE'S NO **CHALLENGE!**

CALLING HER NAMES, TELLING JOKES ABOUT HER... IT'S NOT ANY **FUN** IF THERE'S NO CHANCE SHE'LL SNEAK UP AND **OVERHEAR** ME!

I CAN STAND HERE AND SAY, "MRS. GODFREY IS SO FAT, HER FANNY PACK HAS VINYL SIDING" WITH NO FEAR OF GETTING...

...BUSTED.

DETENTIC

HEY, MISTER, AREN'T YOU THE SPORTSWRITER FROM THE "DAILY BEACON"?

THAT'S RIGHT!

CAN I ASK YOU SOMETHING?

YOU'VE WATCHED HUNDREDS OF GAMES! YOU'VE SEEN ALL THE BEST GOALIES IN THE STATE!

CAN YOU TELL ME HOW TO TAKE MY GAME TO THAT "ELITE" LEVEL?

ANY TIPS, ANY SUGGESTIONS THAT YOU HAVE!... LAY 'EM ON ME!

WELL, THERE IS ONE LITTLE THING...

HOLD IT. LET ME WRITE THIS DOWN.

THIS IS PATHETIC. LOOKING AT JENNY'S HAIR UNDER THE MICROSCOPE HAS **CHANGED** MY **FEELINGS** ABOUT HER!

I CAN'T GET THE NASTY IMAGE OF HER HAIR OUT OF MY MIND! I KNOW IT'S STUPID, BUT I CAN'T **HELP** IT!

AM I REALLY THAT SHALLOW?

YOU GONNA FINISH THOSE?

YES TO BOTH QUESTIONS.

IT'S A PROVEN FACT THAT YAWNING IS CONTAGIOUS!

HM.

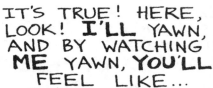

IT'S TRUE! HERE, LOOK! **I'LL** YAWN, AND BY WATCHING **ME** YAWN, **YOU'LL** FEEL LIKE...

EEEYAWNN!

HEY, NOT YET!

DID I HAVE A CHOICE?

NATE, MRS. GODFREY LEFT ME A NOTE ABOUT YOU.

ABOUT **ME?**

SHE SAYS YOU SOMETIMES LIKE TO HAND IN YOUR ASSIGNMENTS IN COMIC BOOK FORMAT.

I PREFER TO THINK OF THEM AS "GRAPHIC NOVELS."

WHATEVER YOU CALL THEM, JUST MAKE SURE THEY'RE HISTORICALLY AND FACTUALLY ACCURATE, ALL RIGHT?

GOTCHA!

THANKSGIVING
:COMIX!:

Plymouth, 1627...

... and after the karaoke contest, we'll have our dwarf-tossing tournament!

Good!

Good!

Hold it.

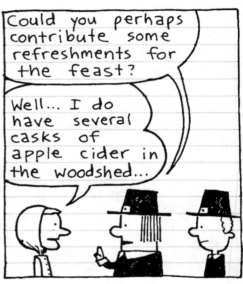

YOU SEE, MR. GAFFNEY, THE FACT THAT THE STUDENTS HAVE GIVEN YOU A NICK-NAME MEANS YOU'VE **MADE** IT!

MADE IT?

YOU'RE NO LONGER THOUGHT OF AS A **SUB**! SUBS DON'T **GET** NICK-NAMES! BUT **REAL** TEACHERS **DO**!

ACCORDING TO WHOM?

ACCORDING TO **ME**! I'M THE COM-MISSIONER OF NICKNAMES!

A SELF-APPOINTED POST, I'M GUESSING.

HEEEEY! **Q**-TIP!

SO WHAT DOES THE "COMMISSIONER OF NICKNAMES" **DO**, EXACTLY?

I KEEP TRACK OF ALL THE NICKNAMES! FOR TEACHERS **AND** KIDS!

SOUNDS LIKE A BIG JOB!

NOT FOR **ME**! I HAVE **TOTAL RECALL** OF ALL NICKNAMES GOING BACK **FIVE YEARS!**

FOR EXAMPLE, FROM MID-APRIL TO LATE MAY OF 2000, MRS. HOLLIS FROM THE COMPUTER LAB WAS CALLED "LIVIN' LA VIDA DONUTS"! AFTER THAT, IT WAS "LOTTA"! AND IN JUNE, WE START-ED CALLING HER "FAT ELVIS"!

HE CAN'T REMEMBER WHO WROTE "POOR RICHARD'S ALMANAC," BUT HE REMEMBERS "FAT ELVIS."

THEN SHE BECAME "McNUGGETS"...

Peirce

WHAT'S **THIS**? COULD IT **BE**?

IT **IS**! I DON'T **BELIEVE** IT! **GINA** IS IN THE **DETENTION ROOM**!!

IMAGINE **THAT**! LOOKS LIKE LITTLE MISS **PERFECT** ISN'T SO PERFECT **AFTER** ALL!

I GUESS YOU CAN'T ACT LIKE YOU'RE **BETTER** THAN ME ANYMORE, **CAN** YOU? WE'RE **BOTH** HERE! WE'RE **EVEN**!

NOW **SPILL** IT, GINA! WHAT DID YOU DO? WHY ARE YOU HERE?

I'M DOING A STORY FOR THE SCHOOL NEWS-PAPER ABOUT SIXTH-GRADE DISCIPLINARY PROBLEMS.

WHAT'S IT LIKE TO BE A CHRONIC SCREW-UP?

OH, HOW I HATE HER.

Dear Dr. Love:
Help! My boyfriend just broke up with me! I'm so sad! I love him so much!

Heartbroken

Dear Heartbroken:
You say you love him. But remember, there's a thin line between love and hate.

Also, love means never having to say you're sorry. Plus, love is a many-splendored thing.

And, of course, love is blind.

IT MAY HAVE BEEN A MISTAKE TO GIVE HIM MY BOOK OF FAMILIAR QUOTATIONS.

Dear Dr. Love,
My girlfriend and I really enjoy board games. Every weekend she comes over and we play Clue, Monopoly, etc.

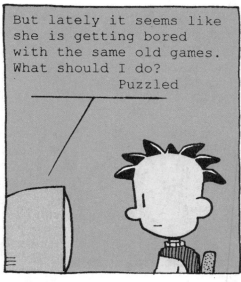

But lately it seems like she is getting bored with the same old games. What should I do?
                    Puzzled

Dear Puzzled:
Get a Life.

Or perhaps a Yahtzee.

AND PEOPLE WONDER WHY NEWS-PAPERS ARE IN DECLINE.